Stella in the Kitchen

Andrea F Nunes

Claudia Emanuele Bernardino

Mariana Ostanik

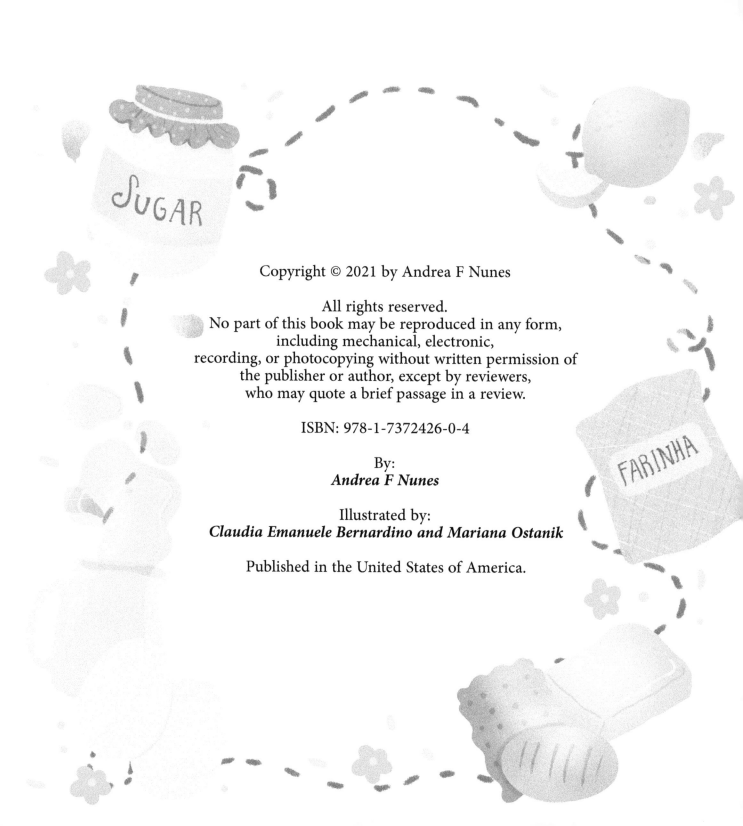

ISBN: 978-1-7372426-0-4

By:
Andrea F Nunes

Illustrated by:
Claudia Emanuele Bernardino and Mariana Ostanik

Published in the United States of America.

Dedicado á minha filha e avós queridos

The big day is here
It's time for some treats
Like grandma's **filhoses**
And **biscoitos** to eat

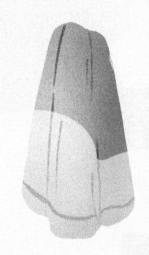

Let's heat up the **forno**
Tie our aprons up
There's lots of good treats
That we have to bake up

Let's start with **farinha**
Some **agua** and yeast
Let's make sure we're making
Enough for a feast

«Amassa a massa!»
Shouts grandma out loud
Let's get the dough rolling
Let's make some good **pão**!

Whip out the **chouriço**
And even some cheese
Let's roll it right in there
This bread's sure to please

"Let's make some **Biscoitos!**"
I say with such pride
They might be my favorite
With **leite** on the side

We need some **açúcar**,
manteiga and eggs,
and water, and flour,
And some lemon zest

Now grab a **tigela**
And a big **colher**
We need to get mixing
and check on the bread!

The **cozinha** smells lovely
The **pão** starts to plump
The **biscoitos** look golden
Then we hear THUMP THUMP

Our **familia** is outside
They knock on the door
It's time to get serving
The treats they adore!

Let's open the oven,
Be careful it's **quente**
Don't touch it without
Putting on oven mitts!

Look at all our goodies
Sweet smelling and warm
They started as **massa**,
Look how they've transformed!